Edmund
and the
Baby Turtles

by Isaac Hales
illustrated by Toby Quarmby

SCHOOL PUBLISHERS

ISBN 10: 0-15-350630-X
ISBN 13: 978-0-15-350630-7

Ordering Options
ISBN 10: 0-15-350598-2 (Grade 1 On-Level Collection)
ISBN 13: 978-0-15-350598-0 (Grade 1 On-Level Collection)
ISBN 10: 0-15-357789-4 (package of 5)
ISBN 13: 978-0-15-357789-5 (package of 5)

11 12 13 14 15   0908   15 14 13 12 11 10

A turtle came out of a lake. She found some soft sand and made a nest with her back feet. Then she laid her eggs. The eggs were all together. The turtle pushed sand on top of her eggs. When her work was done, she went back to the lake.

Many days later, the eggs started to crack. One baby turtle climbed out of its shell and pushed its way out of the nest. The turtle was not safe on the ground. Many animals like to eat baby turtles.

Close by, Edmund and his Uncle Robert were fishing. Edmund's dog, Drum, was sniffing around the edge of the lake. Then Edmund heard Drum barking. Edmund went over to Drum.

Drum had found the baby turtle. It was stuck in some mud.

"Good job, Drum!" said Edmund.

Edmund picked up the turtle. He put it in one of the small pools of water near the lake. It splashed up and down in the fresh water.

Edmund looked around.

"Are there more turtles?" he asked Drum. "We may need to help them, too."

Drum sniffed the ground and tracked the baby turtle's path. Edmund followed.

From the rocks, Uncle Robert
listened for Edmund and Drum.

"Where are you?" he called.

"Watching turtles," answered
Edmund.

Uncle Robert saw them watching
turtles dig their way out of
their nest.

The turtles came out of the sand. Edmund and Uncle Robert watched them walk down to the lake. The turtles reached the water.

"They will be safe now," said Edmund.

"That first turtle should thank you," chuckled Uncle Robert.

"Don't forget Drum!" added Edmund.